Hugg 'n' Bugg

The Surprise

Ian Brown & Eoin Clarke

GRAFFEG

2

Hugg looked about and liked what he saw.
He'd never had so much company before.
His pride was clear for all to see,
Kept neat by Bugg, his fur-dwelling flea.

3

Leopards and pandas and bears and yaks,
Even some beardy goats stopped for a chat.
Hugg looked his finest, all would say,
As he prepared for a special day...

But when the day came,
on their home mountain range,
Things looked different and rather strange.
Everywhere Hugg cast his eye,
Amazing hairstyles passed him by.

6

Yaks with curls, leopards with fringes.
Red pandas sporting rainbow tinges,
Fancy beards on each passing goat,
And even a bear with a stripey coat.

"Bugg, what's happened? Is this your work?
I feel so betrayed I could go berserk!
Outshone on my BIRTHDAY, when only I should look grand!"
"Don't be jealous," said Bugg. "You don't understand."

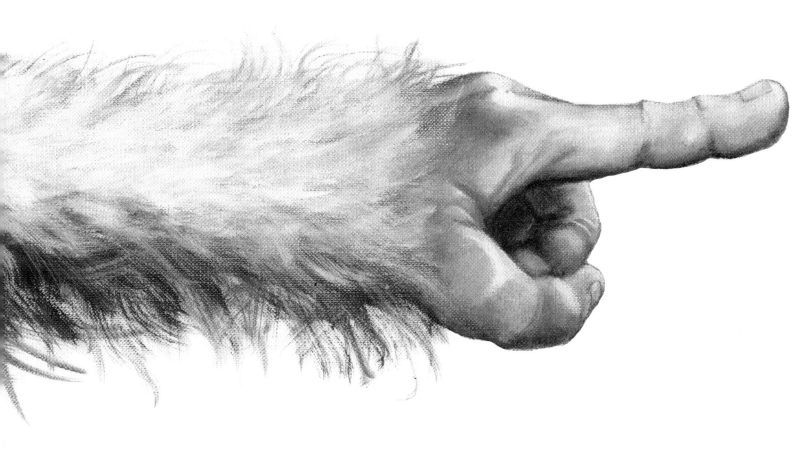

Hugg stormed off in a mighty huff,
But before he'd gone far he looked a terrible scruff.
His coat untamed (even with his hair net),
Hugg was soon full of regret.

"How silly I was to rant and complain,
I need to find Bugg so I can explain."
Hugg set off to find his hairdressing chum,
Searching high and low, still feeling glum.

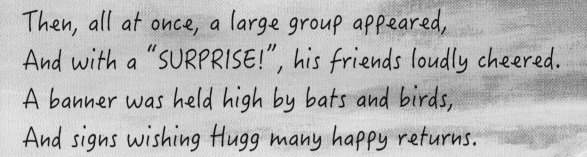

Then, all at once, a large group appeared,
And with a "SURPRISE!", his friends loudly cheered.
A banner was held high by bats and birds,
And signs wishing Hugg many happy returns.

15

A party began, with all in the mood
To eat their way through a mountain of food,
But Hugg had to comment, before they tucked in,
That some of the food looked a little bit grim.

17

18

Bugg sighed and said, "Please don't ask.
This party has not been the easiest task.
Red pandas and yaks are not natural bakers.
Goats don't excel with sugar shakers."

19

"While your birthday party is thoroughly earned,
There have been many lessons learned.
Who knew so much could go wrong mid-flight
When you trust bats to transport a creamy light bite?"

"You see, dear Hugg, there's no mystery.
This is the biggest party in our history.
Everything's been laid on to honour you,
And all wanted to look smart for your special do."

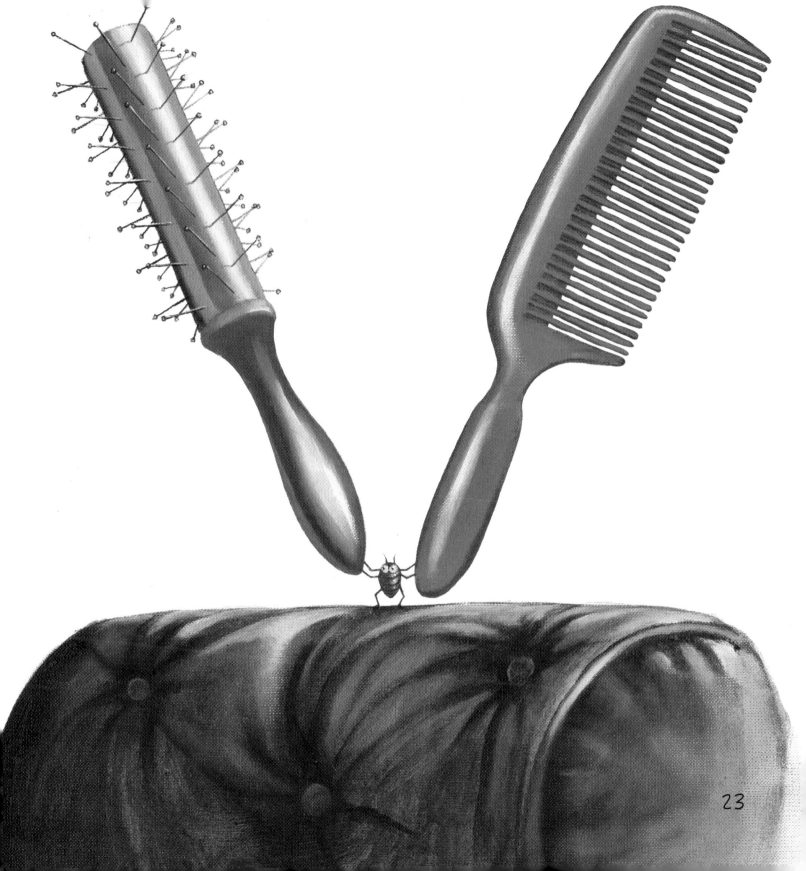

"Hugg, you are my very best friend,
That will be the case until the very end,
But I have friendship and time to spare,
To tend to both yours and others' hair."

25

Hugg said, "Now that my belly is filling with food,
I have to thank you all for lifting my mood.
I'm sorry I made such a jealous fuss,
But now I trust there will always be us."

28

"Thank you, Hugg, I'm glad you see,
We can all be friends and can both agree,
That just because we're closer than most,
You can still be a friendly host."

29

Hugg smiled, and all gave a round of applause,
But all of a sudden the big yeti paused.
"Little Bugg," said Hugg, "I don't mean to be rude,
But I can see a hare right there in my food!"

30

"The hopping sort with floppy ears!
But it's my first birthday cake in
all of my years,
So let's tuck in and enjoy this day.
A hare in my food is quite OK."

Ian Brown

Ian is a former journalist, turned television writer and producer. After a spell on local and national newspapers, a thirty-year career in television has included news, documentaries, commercials, comedy and entertainment shows. He has written or produced for a host of household names, picking up several awards along the way. He's also often heard on radio talking about television. Writing for children has been a long-held dream. Ian shares his home with, among others, wife Millie, two cats and a tortoise – called Albert. You can join Hugg 'n' Bugg on Facebook: @HUGGnBUGG.

Eoin Clarke

Eoin qualified with a BA in Graphic Design from Middlesex University and an MA in Animation from the Royal College of Art. He has worked for thirty years in the animation industry as a director, animator, designer and storyboard artist. He has directed films, commercials, documentaries and title sequences and has picked up thirty awards as a director, working on projects for, among others, the BBC, Channel 4 and the British Film Institute.

Also in this series:

Hugg 'n' Bugg: Finding Home
ISBN 9781802582000

Hugg 'n' Bugg: The Comb
ISBN 9781802583069

Other books by Ian Brown and Eoin Clarke:

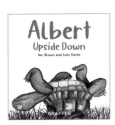

Albert Upside Down
ISBN 9781802586787

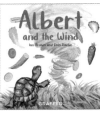

Albert and the Wind
ISBN 9781913733445

Albert and the Pond
ISBN 9781802587296

Albert Supersize
ISBN 9781802580167

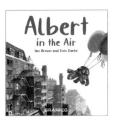

Albert in the Air
ISBN 9781802580174

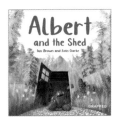

Albert and the Shed
ISBN 9781802585001

Hugg 'n' Bugg: The Surprise
Published in Great Britain in 2024 by Graffeg Limited.

ISBN 9781802586817

Written by Ian Brown copyright © 2024.
Illustrated by Eoin Clarke copyright © 2024.
Designed and produced by Graffeg Limited
copyright © 2024.

Graffeg Limited, 15 Neptune Court, Vanguard Way, Cardiff,
CF24 5PJ, Wales. UK. Tel: +44(0)1554 824000.
www.graffeg.com.

36